To Lisa
No kisses but
I still love ya.
aunt Sandy
and
annisa

Lisa
Did
this 😊

😊

This book belongs to:

LISa coLLeen

June 15, 1983

Mary Cartwright's

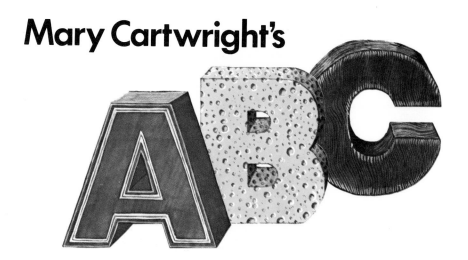

RAND McNALLY & COMPANY

Chicago • New York • San Francisco

First printing, 1981

Published in the U.S.A. in 1981 by
Rand McNally & Company

Illustrations copyright © 1979 Mary Cartwright
Text copyright © 1979 Pumpkin Press London/PS Productions Amsterdam

SBN 528-82405-8

Printed in the United States of America by
Rand McNally & Company
Library of Congress Catalog Card Number: 81-50991

Aa

admiral

anchor

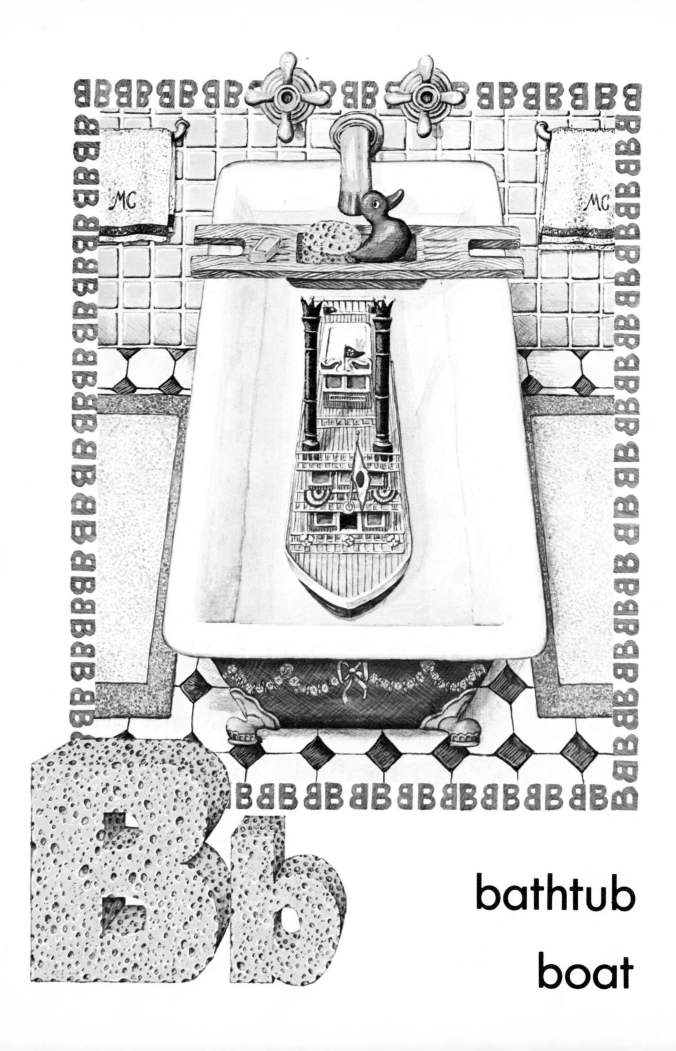

bathtub

boat

cactus

cowboy

diamond
dolphin

elk

Eskimo

flamingo
fortress

giraffe

gondola

hedge

helicopter

igloo

Indian

jewels
jockey

kaleidoscope

kangaroo

lion

locomotive

mandarin

mask

nest

nut

oasis

orchestra

palace

parrot

queen

quilt

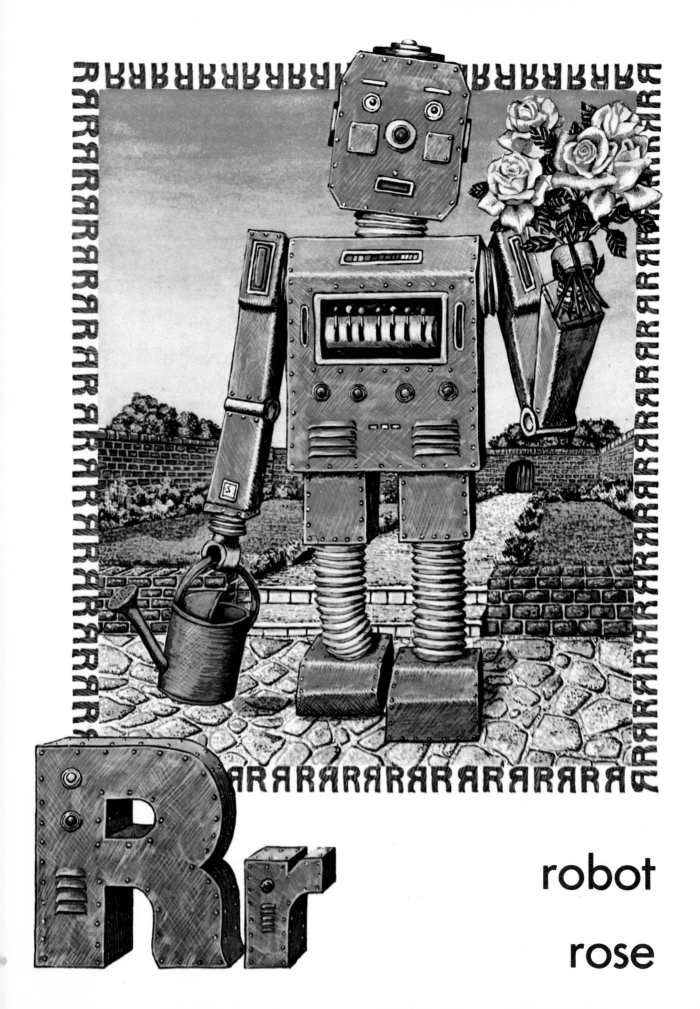

robot

rose

S s

shoe
soldier

tower
tulip

ukulele

uniform

violet

violin

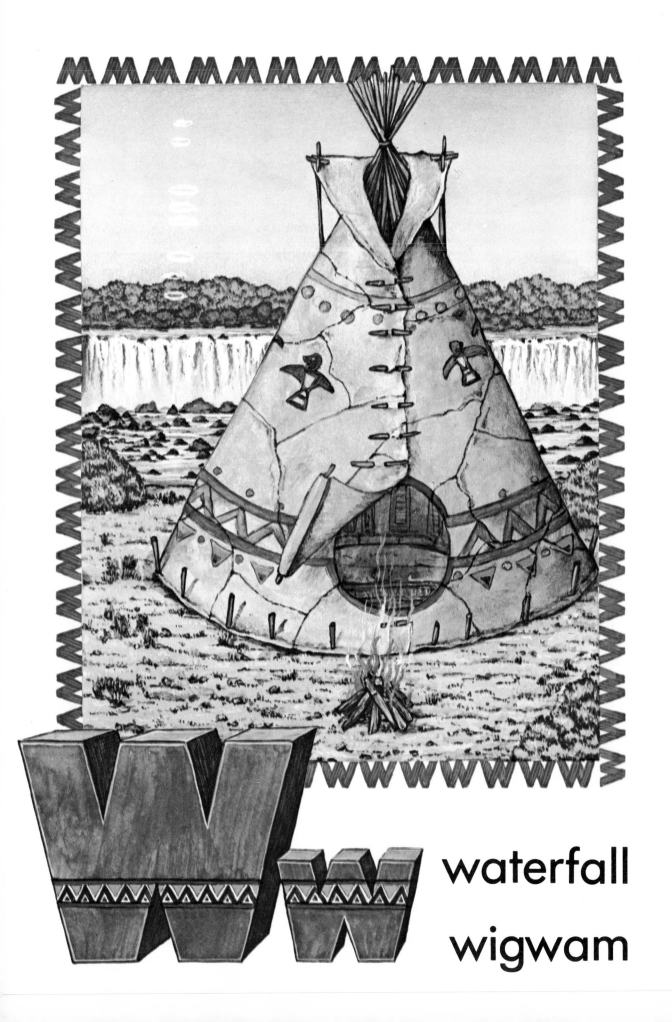

waterfall

wigwam

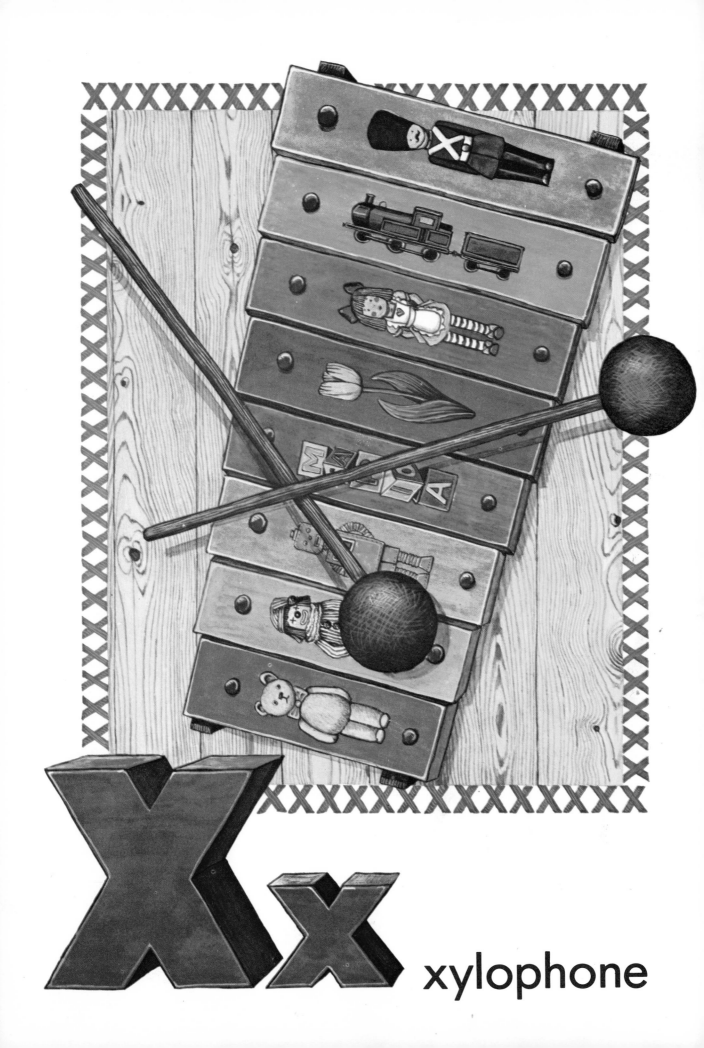

xylophone

yak

yucca

zebra

zoo

About the Artist

Born in Luton, England, on January 10, 1955, Mary Cartwright has always had a love and fascination for children's books.

Having completed a foundation course in art and design at college in Luton, Mary went to London and worked as a nanny for just over a year. Then, the desire to become a weaver took her to Hereford College of Art, where in 1975 she studied textiles and became interested in illustration. In her final year Mary was already accepting commissions, and by the time she left college, she had sufficient work to become a full-time free-lance illustrator.

Mary now lives in a farmhouse in Herefordshire, England, surrounded by children's books and her two cats, Possum and George. Her self-taught style of illustration is unique and reveals her obvious pleasure and ability in illustrating books for children.

Mary Cartwright's 1 2 3

Also published with Mary Cartwright's A B C is Mary Cartwright's 1 2 3. A beautifully illustrated counting book, Mary Cartwright's 1 2 3 will delight and amuse children and parents alike and will be a prized addition to any child's bookshelf.